Fifteen on a Spring Day

Written by Cheryl Blinston **15** Illustrated by Hala Wittwer

Spring is my favorite time of year.

I love to hear the birds singing.
Count the birds. Do you count 15?

I love to see the earthworms wiggle after a spring rain. Count the earthworms.
Do you count 15?

I love to feel the soft fur of puppies.
Count the puppies. Do you count 15?

I love to smell the flowers in bloom.
Count the flowers. Do you count 15?

But most of all I love the taste of ice cream on a warm spring day. How many scoops of ice cream can you count?